"Prithee hark . . ."

The Hokinson Festival

WITH A MEMOIR BY
JAMES REID PARKER
AND AN APPRECIATION BY
JOHN MASON BROWN

E. P. Dutton & Company, Inc.
New York

COPYRIGHT, ©, 1956

By The Estate of HELEN E. HOKINSON

All rights reserved

PRINTED IN THE U. S. A.

No part of this book may be reproduced in any form without permission in writing from the publisher, except by a reviewer who wishes to quote brief passages in connection with a review written for inclusion in magazine or newspaper or radio broadcast.

THE HOKINSON FESTIVAL was compiled from earlier books previously copyrighted as follows:

My Best Girls, ©,1941, E. P. Dutton & Co., Inc.

When Were You Built? ©, 1948, Helen E. Hokinson

The Ladies, God Bless 'em! ©,1950 by the Estate of Helen E. Hokinson

There Are Ladies Present ©, 1952 by the Estate of Helen E. Hokinson

Library of Congress Catalog Card Number: 56-11240

Publisher's Note

Since Miss Hokinson's characters are so enchantingly timeless, her publishers have never felt tempted to present in a rigid chronological order the drawings in any Hokinson book. After all, in Miss Hokinson's world very little alters except the hemline, and even this moves upward and downward only with the greatest circumspection. It should perhaps be mentioned, however, that when our artist's ladies are busy with national-defense activities, the period is that of the Second World War; apart from this, Miss Hokinson's characters are above both rubies and too-precise dates.

Mr. James Reid Parker, who wrote most of the original captions, has had occasion to make fewer than a dozen changes — usually consisting of no more than a word or two — for the sake of clarity in this year of grace.

All the drawings in this book first appeared in *The New Yorker,* and grateful acknowledgment is made for permission to reproduce them.

The Hokinson Festival

"I forget — is it the Critics' Prize or the Pulitzer Prize that you don't have to pay any attention to?"

"It's the same lecture, but for the twenty dollars extra he wears a leopard skin."

"Remember, we're having our mental cocktail next Thursday — John Mason Brown!"

"Does this ticket entitle me to a hangover in Philadelphia?"

"We can't make up our minds whether to buy or build."

"I hope I haven't alarmed you about Dartmouth."

"I'm afraid Madame Brown isn't _thinking_ in French."

Helen E. Hokinson

"*Do you think if we all got together we could persuade Mr. Kirby to carry gluten bread?*"

"Don't be selfish dear, Mother needs a daiquiri."

"But a cactus never does anything."

*"Why, I'm thrilled! I had no idea the Philharmonic
was throwing in Horowitz today!"*

"They all involve *stooping*, don't they?"

"Hello, badminton champion!"

"*Joyeux Noël, my good man!*"

"*I wish I'd known you were going to dress up.*"

"We're looking for a fourth — someone who doesn't play very well."

"Oh, George! Remember the very jolly couple we met at the Futurama?"

"Do you go to Hearns?"

"Now, when Parker beats, the old year will have gone."

"You don't ever tell anyone what I read, do you?"

"I hope this isn't going to _emphasize_ anything."

*"What do you say, everybody? Shall we dispense with
the Southern accent altogether?"*

"By the way, did the Queen ever write Mrs. Roosevelt a bread-and-butter letter?"

"I thought somebody like Noel Coward might be able to use it."

"She isn't __really__ quaint at all. She's a college graduate."

"Hugh Walpole liked it, Fanny Butcher liked it, Wm. Rose Benét liked it, and Mrs. Roosevelt liked it, but it _isn't_ very good."

"Come early. We're going to experiment with mint juleps."

"D.A.R.'s?"
"No, cherry blossoms."

Helen E. Hokinson

"Mr. Martin, you must sit down and tell Mrs. Potter
exactly what it is you do."

"Aren't we going to toot?"

"I'm punishing myself for being a naughty girl yesterday in Schrafft's."

"My dollar-and-a-half pills are doing me so much good."

*"I hope, dear, you won't
come back from Vassar with a lot of <u>ideas</u>."*

"Personally, I <u>like</u> to see a nervous bride."

"I hope the Red Cross doesn't
hear of my sneaking off without my knitting."

"Speyer Hospital! And drive like mad!"

"Would it help, dear, if I played
a little Beethoven?"

"I understand the thing to do first is to drink _oceans_
of hot buttered rum."

"*Mrs. Conklin says that if we give her a free hand, she can easily make it into a rumpus room.*"

"*I warn you, my right foot is a rebel.*"

"*Dear, I wish you'd say something nice
to Victoria. I'm afraid she's catching a cold.*"

"But __is__ a horse more loyal?"

"I'm for the action back only if you're going to do something."

"What would you recommend? I'm just a beginner."

"And then in May we go to a dear little Hansel-and-Gretel house
in a town called Westport."

"You don't want the blue uniform,
nor the gray, nor the maroon. Now, Joseph, what _do_ you want?"

"And when they spawn, do I do anything?"

"We planned Chester very carefully."

"Can you make me look like anything at all by four-thirty?"

"You are to be congratulated on your custard pie."

"Burton Holmes always leaves me so restless."

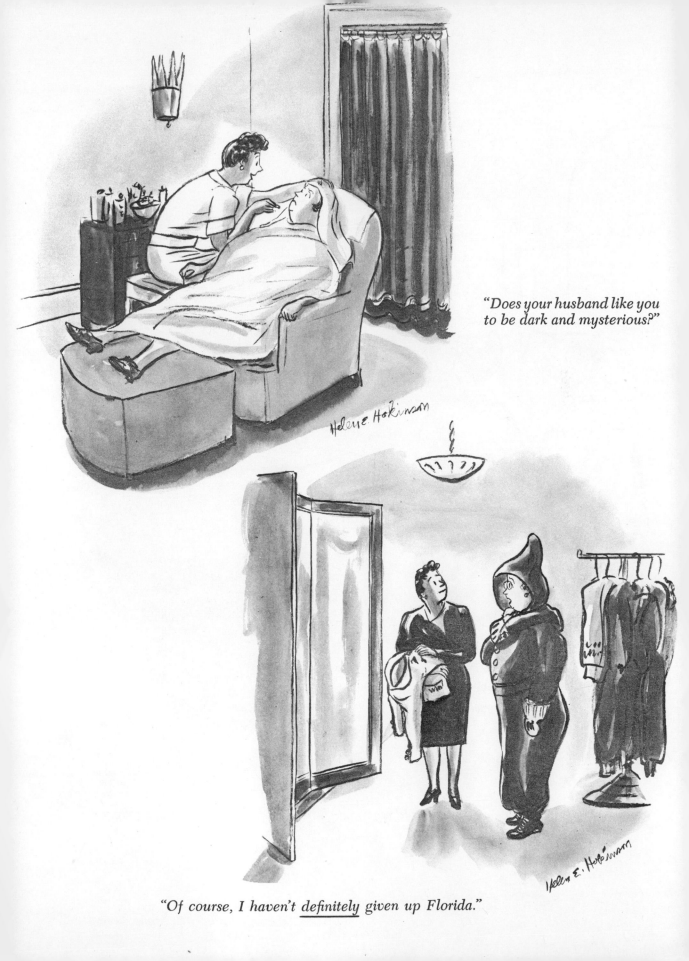

"Does your husband like you to be dark and mysterious?"

"Of course, I haven't __definitely__ given up Florida."

"You'd think George and Ella would try to patch things up for the children's sake."

"You mean my zinc may go up _because_ of Mr. Roosevelt?"

"Have you strengthened the second act?"

"Can't you think of *anything* McGinnis could do?"

"If you don't want to look for shells, what *do* you want to do?"

"I don't think he's even trying."

"I'm afraid I've made a perfectly terrible mistake. See if you notice anything."

"We were very disappointed in Edmund's horoscope. We hoped it would say he was artistic, or at <u>least</u> musical."

"My big problem now is where to go this summer."

"I want you to do something about his rumba. It's perfectly terrible!"

"Well, if I'm not Magda Lupescu, who <u>am</u> I?"

"When we get back to New York, let's all start going to Columbia."

"The purser was born in Edinburgh. When he was a boy he ran away to sea. He's married and has two children. I happened to run into him on the boat deck."

*"Can you tell me which one of these levers I pull to vote
<u>against</u> the present administration?"*

"What would you suggest for three hungry bears?"

"You aren't doing this just because you're mad at Connecticut, are you?"

"Well, if Mildred doesn't show up,
we'll just have to amuse each other."

"The facial is two dollars, but for 50 cents more, Attilio will go down your spine."

"Does a begonia go on and on?"

"Perhaps we shouldn't listen. I believe he's trying to influence our vote."

"After all, dear, <u>Harry Hansen</u> couldn't put it down until he finished it."

*"George guess what, the superintendent
says I can tap dance until people complain."*

"Hello, A. & P. We're back!"

"Well, I don't know . . ."

"I could kick myself for not stopping when I *had it*."

"I'm really only going in to phone."

"Now where has our lucky ball gone to?"

"I like what you've been saying about Lindbergh."

"There's a certain party I'd like to see put off the ice."

"We've come to see the Queen."

"Now stop frowning,
Mrs. Yates, or I'll have to take that
'New Republic' away from you."

"I'm sorry, Madam President, there won't be any treasurer's report this month because we have a deficit."

"This year I want lighthearted slipcovers."

"I don't like murders that take place in New Jersey."

"Could you tell us which path Thoreau used to take?"

...and reason, Madam. What kind of goldfish could it be that a drugstore gives away free with a ten-cent tube of toothpaste?"

"Can't I go back to _birds?_"

"The Garden Committee reports that Mrs. Bernard Thayer, Mrs. Harrison S. Quigley,
and Mrs. Thompson Sperry have all seen pussy willows."

"Help! I've changed my mind!"

"I've been driving for a whole
year, and you're the very first person
who hasn't got out of my way."

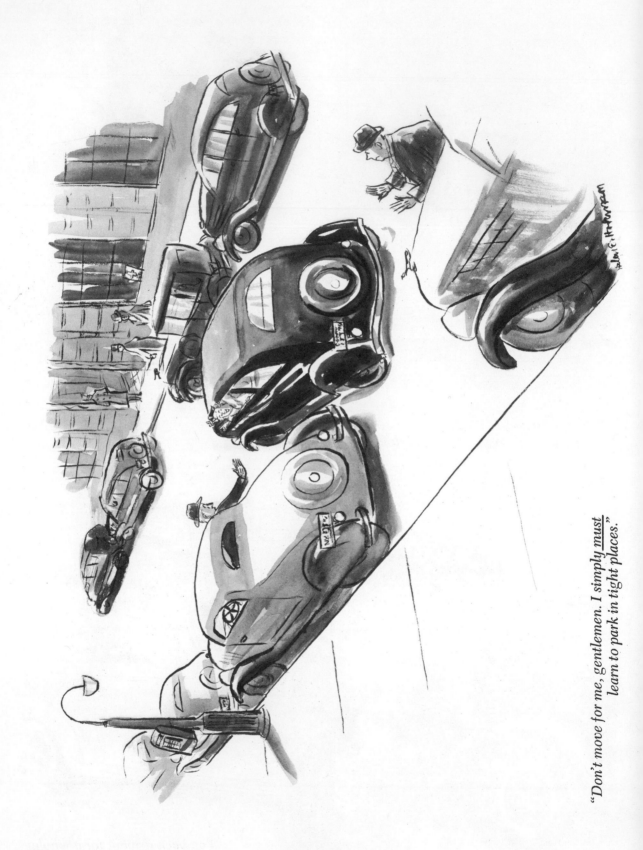

"Don't move for me, gentlemen. I simply must learn to park in tight places."

"Does Mignon G. Eberhart still use poison?"

"You mean I don't get <u>anything</u> back on the bottles?"

"I'm thinking very seriously of putting Ingeborg into burgundy."

"You mean we're going to be cooped up in <u>America</u> all winter?"

"Dr. MacGruder says I must build myself up before I start reducing."

"__I'm__ the one that should be lying down somewhere."

"Oh, Madam mustn't _fight_ her way into it."

"Sometimes Winnie's for sale, and sometimes she isn't."

"This is one by Dwight Fiske. The children love it, but personally
I don't think it makes much sense."

"Aiken, my Aiken!"

"Albert, I did something wrong on the George Washington Bridge."

"I put it down here <u>somewhere</u>."

"*Would it be cheating if I told you where the ball is?*"

"I'm <u>so</u> glad you asked God to Guide Mr. Roosevelt."

—Helen E. Hokinson

"I'm taking lots of pictures of you, Mr. Gilroy,
so as to make my husband jealous."

"Are you sure you aren't making a mistake? Groton may change with Dr. Peabody gone."

"They sleep like that for hours. Shall we watch him a while?"

*"Just a minute. I'm going to ask him a question
or two about Mrs. Luhan."*

"You aren't going to need this Yale crew sweater again, are you, Osgood?"

*"Alan, show Mrs. Gibson your rejection
slip from the Atlantic Monthly."*

*"It's perfectly
simple. Just
go to Altman's and ask for the corset
that Mrs. Jones of Chappaqua wears."*

"Let's not complain about the cream. Let's complain about the French dressing."

"Oh, Hulda! I was going to surprise you."

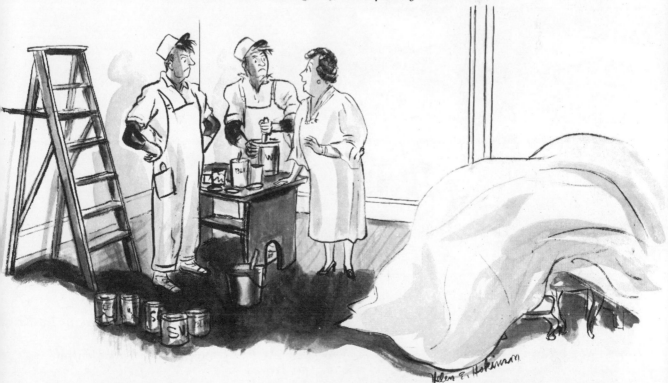

"Do you happen to remember the exquisite violet of the Perisphere at night?"

"Listen, lug, I'm giving you just one hour to get out of town —"

"They didn't charge extra for Ry-Krisp

on the New York Central."

"I'm looking for something in which to put a lock of hair."

"*There is no Santa Claus. Gimbel's always tells the truth.*"

*"Life says that it will send a photographer to our cake sale
if it possibly can."*

"... music, dramatics, careful health supervision, organized play, a thirteen-acre campus studded with fine old maples. Character and individuality are stressed ..."

"Can't you put down that detective story for even a minute, George? You're supposed to be on a vacation."

"Why, I'm Sadie Thompson—you know, that girl in a play."

"I've come to get my Easter face."

"Buon giorno, Scuola Berlitz. Il Signor Esposito, per favore."

"There must be something in Tiffany's a young ensign
could use on a minesweeper."

"*Please tell Mrs. Anderson to cast on forty Germantown. Then join French Zephyr. First two rows, knit one, purl one, with Germantown; second two, knit one, purl one, with Zephyr. Then repeat. I'm sure she'll have no trouble.*"

"Oh, I forgot to tell you. Come as <u>pirates</u>."

"When were you built?"

"I just want to say that I'm perfectly willing to serve as treasurer, provided every penny doesn't have to come out exactly even."

"Then how _do_ you intend to get to house furnishings?"

*"The question is, do we want to fall
back on Gilbert and Sullivan or do we want to fall back on Ibsen?"*

"Hasn't Silvermine just gobs of atmosphere!"

"It isn't that there aren't plenty of men in Vermont, it's just that you have to <u>look</u> for them."

"I often wish I'd kept up my mandolin lessons."

"I suppose I ought to gi
Jackson & Perkins some
the credit."

"I never know how
far-away to stand to make
them look good."

"Anyone else going to the Martha Washington?"

"I never give *my* roses stimulants."

"I like poetry, all rig[...]
but I hate to pay five cents a day for [...]

"Is it all right for an expectant mother to catch chipmunks?"

"But there are only seven more treatments in the course, Mrs. Freeman. We mustn't throw in the sponge now!"

I've decided to give Louis Bromfield another chance."

"But __why__ isn't a major fish, flesh, fowl, or good red herring, dear?"

"Now, don't worry, dear. I'm hoping I won't see anything I like."

"Now, the first thing we must ask ourselves is 'Why is the gazelle supple?'"

"Excuse me. Do you happen to know what a porcupine symbolizes?"

"Does it matter which end we do them from?"

"It's an allegory. You have to be feeling unreal to enjoy it."

"Of course, you'd have to have a castle or something."

". . and just a block away there was the most wonderful
le restaurant, where they had lobsters and artichokes
only nine francs, and we went there every single day."

"'Aurora, seated on a cloud with a cupid who
olds a torch, looks down at Cephalus, who . . .'"

"Can't you remember _anything_
but the blood that ran out of the horse?"

Helen E. Hokinson

*"Would this be all right for
a friend who isn't interested in much of anything?"*

". . . and the little flower pocket definitely takes it out of the kitchen."

*"Well, if your husband isn't going to be
at Hot Springs, either, we can get in all sorts of mischief."*

"Now don't be timid. George tells me the Yale Club <u>wants</u> women."

"Oh, dear! Here come those napkins I wasn't going to buy."

"You mean we still haven't liberated that place where my tea comes from?"

"What's Prince Matchabe
up to this year?"

"It irritates me when the corpse
doesn't have any visible injuries
at _all_."

"But it isn't *supposed* to make sense!"

"I have a little rule about not discussing Russia
at the dinner table."

"Of course, I wouldn't want a card that says too much."

"But does Westchester want a strong Yugoslavia?"

"I know who she'd be crazy about — that little
Mitchell dog up in Scarsdale."

"Oh, I disagree. I think there
are lots of cute candidates this year!"

*"Go away. You're
rattling me."*

"Do you mind if we sing just <u>one</u> Smith song?"

"Now don't let me
speak another word of English!"

"But there's not much point
to looking exotic in Englewood."

"Is anybody Alice Pomeroy, Swarthmore, 1913?"

"Mrs. Brown acts so harassed lately. Do you suppose she's really found a maid?"

"We've decided to allow our canary to become a mother"

"Have you any <u>serious</u> ashtrays?"

"If everything has a funny taste, don't worry. It's just herbs."

"Guess what Victoria said today — she said 'please.'"

"Of course, they're just at the awkward age"

"Perhaps if Madam would try
to meet it halfway . ."

"Tonight I think I'll go to bed _before_ the murder."

"Surely you can't have misplaced the Eighteenth Armored Division *again*, Miss MacEldowny!"

"Elizabeth Connor McMeekin, '15?"

"Present. After graduation, I started to take an M.A. at Teachers College, but gave it up to marry Ro[...] [M]cMeekin, Cornell, '12. My husband was only a plant engineer with the telephone company at the tim[e] [an]d had not yet become an executive. We lived in Columbus, Ohio, until 1927, when Mr. McMeekin wa[s] [cal]led to New York, and we built a home in Westchester. I have two children, a girl, Elsie, aged nineteen, [an]d a boy, Donald, aged seventeen. I want to say that I think this Alpha Delta Alpha alumnae picnic is a [wo]nderful idea and that Penny Trowbridge should be congratulated on getting it up. I hope we can ge[t] [to]gether next summer and repeat it with all the same people."

"It isn't that Macy's dislikes Gimbel's, it's just that Macy's prefers upholster its chairs with its own fabrics."

"New Canaan isn't really in the country. It only looks like the country."

"Norman, let's start talking about Christmas."

"Oh, I always send condolences — providing I've <u>known</u> the dog."

"I'm sorry, but I am murdering Mr. Hodgson to the best of my ability!"

"*I know what! Let's have an Old-Fashioned before we start talking French.*"

"*...re aren't any bulls who would object to my blouse, are there?*"

"Let the birthday girl go first!"

"Now, remember. Pretend you <u>hate</u> Staffordshire!"

"I'm going to be here for only two weeks, and I want clams, clams, clams!"

", Colonel, when you say
life as we know it in
stchester is doomed, surely
mean it *humorously?*"

"Well, the truth is,
I'm lukewarm about insane asylums."

*"A very dear friend gave me some wonderful old
Scotch, and there just happened to be a bottle of papaya juice in the icebox."*

'raid this is goodbye, Miss MacDonald. I'm joining the Book-of-the-Month Club.

"Mr. Dodd and I just want you to cook very simple meals, do a little dusting and bed-making, and be happy."

"Do try to appear calm and matter-of-fact. First impressions are very important."

*"I wonder if I could enlist your coöperation in a little
scheme I have for livening up my husband."*

"...that's what that Mr. Smith does. I never realized
he didn't have to earn a living."

"Let's try a sixteen and see what happens."

"n what floor do I find the hats for better women?"

"Personally, I think Madam look
better in the palm trees than
in the wild geese."

"My husband has very definite ideas. He doesn't want me
to look like a mushroom or ā rabbit."

e treasurer wants me to announce that unless some of the members pay
their back dues, she will simply lose her mind."

"What are the <u>women</u> of distinction drinking?"

"I've put you next to a man who may or may not be dangerous."

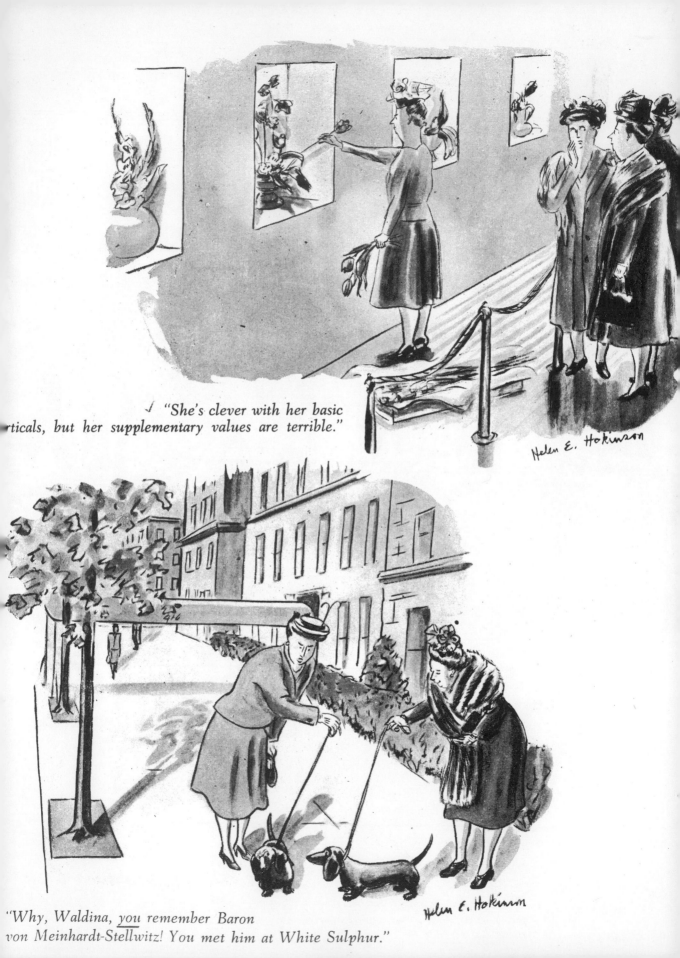

"She's clever with her basic verticals, but her supplementary values are terrible."

Helen E. Hokinson

"Why, Waldina, _you_ remember Baron von Meinhardt-Stellwitz! You met him at White Sulphur."

Helen E. Hokinson

"...ankly, I've reached the stage where I don't care whether stripes are vertical or not."

"Let's try the Débutante Department, just on a wild gamble."

"Of course, you understand these measurements are only temporary."

"...n't know, I sort of hate to waste a facial
on the New Friends of Music."

"Goodness! Isn't Chile _thin_!"

"Eric Sevareid was every bit as surprised as I was."

"...ll me, Admiral,
...ich is your favorite ocean?"

"...u want the works, I suppose."

"How can I persuade some very undesirable starlings to move?"

"You mean I can buy some bonds from you sitting right here on this sofa?"

*"Madam is really very nice
when she's all together."*

"*After hearing Colonel Morgan, I'm sure all of us have overcome any fear we may have had of Russia*"

"*I insist! After all, summoning four ghosts from the past was my idea.*"

"Why, yes, Mr. Stimson *did* call you a few days ago and wanted
you to call him back, but *I* forgot to tell you because of some
trouble I was having with a tooth."

"*Would you sanction a tôle breaabasket as a container for portulaca?*"

"*I just love doing this — it takes my mind off the war.*"

"A strange woman is sitting in our corner of the porch."

"How can seven people have fun?"

"...want something that will last ...bout five hours."

"...ou don't by any remote chance happen ... to be Brahms lovers, do you?"

"I'm still not satisfied with _anyone's_ kisses!"

"I wouldn't want to go to Trinidad unless you're sure there'd be somebody else there."

"We're the Eight Reckless Bidders and we have a reservation."

"I've lost a little hat shop."

"Is everybody ready for the Venezuelan national drink?"

"Oh, dear, I hope Consolidated Edison
hasn't done something foolish!"

"They're terribly strict in here about soliciting. You can set your can on the table, but they won't let you shake it."

"Herbert, why can't we collect a little painter who'll be good someday?"

"I feel sorry for Mississippi, but I just don't like to read about it"

Helen E. Hokinson

"Would you mind taking in two drowned rats?"

"This won't change my thinking, will it

"Haven't you got something I could just squeeze or push?"

"Oh dear!"

"It's to pour over grapefruit."

"I really expected to look a little different for twenty-eight dollars."

"George, why don't we ever go to places like Cartier's and just look around?

"Now, please bear in mind that I am _not_ Ingrid Bergman."

nd this one means that you beseech the sun god to ripen the corn."

"Why is *this* cigar any better than *that* cigar?"

Helen E. Hokinson

"Right after church we're going to try hot buttered rum made with oleo."

"*Before I introduce Mr. Garrison, I ought to mention something. He's had I don't know how many wives, but it wasn't his fault.*"

"Oh, did I tell you about the perfectly lovely compliment a saleswoman in Bonwit's coat department paid me this afternoon?"

"There's something I want to ask you, Colonel. Would the Army like to know how to make Spam interesting?"

Helen E Hokinson

"I don't know how everybody else feels, but <u>I</u> feel like weeding."

*"I'll tell you one thing — Henry James wasn't <u>worth</u>
a forty-seven-cent fine."*

"Harvey, do you __really__ like the Dodgers, or is it just a pose?"

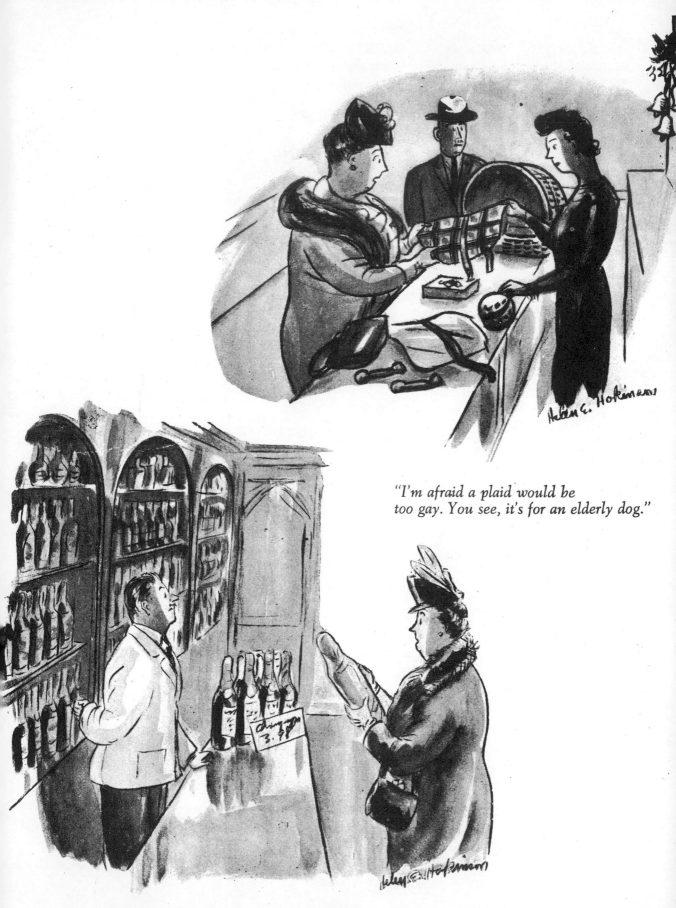

"I'm afraid a plaid would be
too gay. You see, it's for an elderly dog."

"I suppose the directions are on the bottle."

don't mind the American Revolution as long as it
doesn't have too much sex in it."

"What do you think, George! You're giving me
nething for Christmas that you won't have to pay for all at once."

"The taxis are pretending they don't see me."

"If there are any of those deductions I'm not entitled to, don't hesitate to say so."

"Which is the vitamin
 that takes the place of Florid[a]"

"Which do you think is more Christmassy?
Tammany Hall one hundred years ago or a
panda?"

"It overwhelmed Brooks Atkinson, but it isn't overwhelming me."

"We want to send a hostess
present to a dachshund."

". . . and then I covered them
that was the last I ever saw of them."

"Martha, I hope you're going to be as thrilled by this news as I am. I've just inherited a farm!"

"My husband is going to be the most surprised man in Plainfield."

"If you should happen to be in Plummer's at any time, Mr. Robinson on the second floor knows what I want for Christmas."

"Isn't it about time another one of John Gunther's 'Insides' came out?"

"My red spiders _liked_ your rotenone dust!"

"I don't really _like_ Bach, but I respect him."

Waiting to be told that whatever they want is not to be found.

A reading-room siren

LIBRARY
FAUNA

One o'clock

SCHOOL
DAYS

"You know perfectly well, Louise, that six and four are not eleven."

H. S. Hutchinson

"Is life so sweet, comma, or peace so dear, comma . . . ?"

An advanced student

*"I thought you said there weren't **any** fascinating men left in Oyster Bay."*

"We come here every summer. George was born
on a farm, you know."

*"I believe we're next
door. Aren't you the apartment with dinner chimes?"*

*"Of course some cats have eight kittens
but I never have more than six."*

"I loved it where she said she'd never give him up—never, never, never!"

"Since you're out there, young man, will you please give those poor little birds their luncheon?"

"Of course, we don't very often hear of an elopement in our set."

"Henry! Are you listening or are you just thinking?"

"Do you smell something burning?"

"I'm so glad to meet you, Mr. Hutchins. I want to tell you how much I enjoyed wading through your last book."

"I want you to meet a charming vote I've rounded up for you."

"Why, I'd love an Armenian! Are they any good?"

*"What do you think—should I plunge
right into all the Iron Curtain countries or just take up Czechoslovakia?"*

*"Then she told Gary Cooper she could
never love him, and Gary Cooper winced."*

"Is that clock right?"

"I tell you what you _could_ do. You
could load yourself down with costume jewelry."

"Our straw vote has resulted in nineteen votes for the Republicans and one for the Democrats."

"How perfectly uncanny! My Greek is coming back to me."

"Let's see—
they make something
here, don't they?"

"Edmund, are you a bull or a bear? You've
never told me."

"Now, don't make me meet *everyone* in Southampton!"

"George, I have a confession to make. We own a thousand bushels of September wheat."

"Would it surprise you to hear that I composed a club song at Mt. Desert?"

Helen E. Hokinson

*"Jack and I are going all over creation this summer—if
we can sublet our apartment."*

"I'd never let a doll of mine wear a dress like that."

"I suppose you develop
a sixth sense, or something."

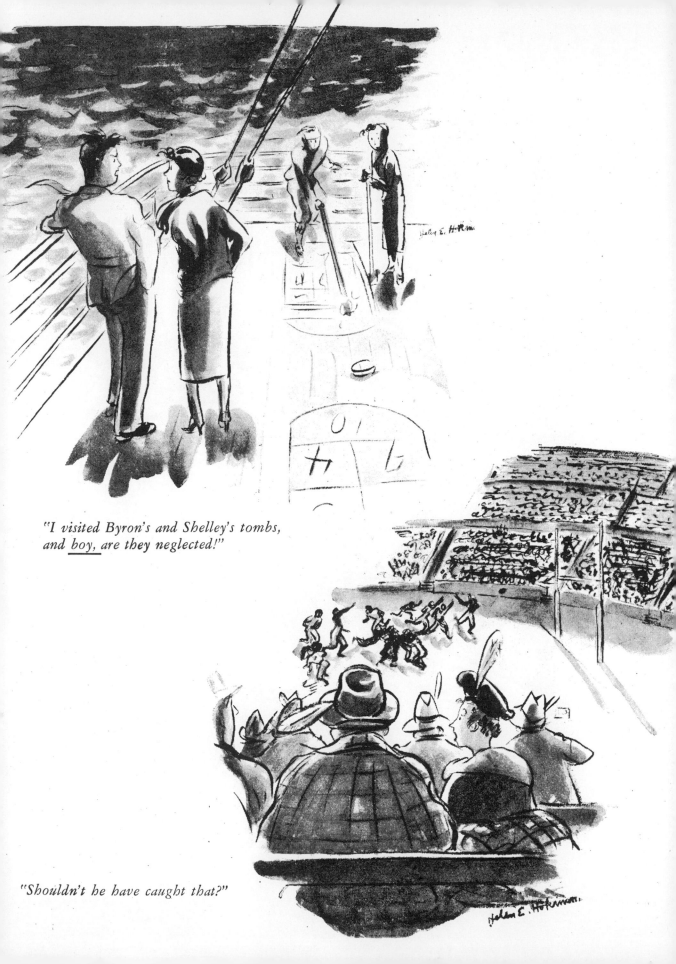

"I visited Byron's and Shelley's tombs, and _boy_, are they neglected!"

"Shouldn't he have caught that?"

"And the Swami says if everyone only
breathed properly, we wouldn't have all these wars."

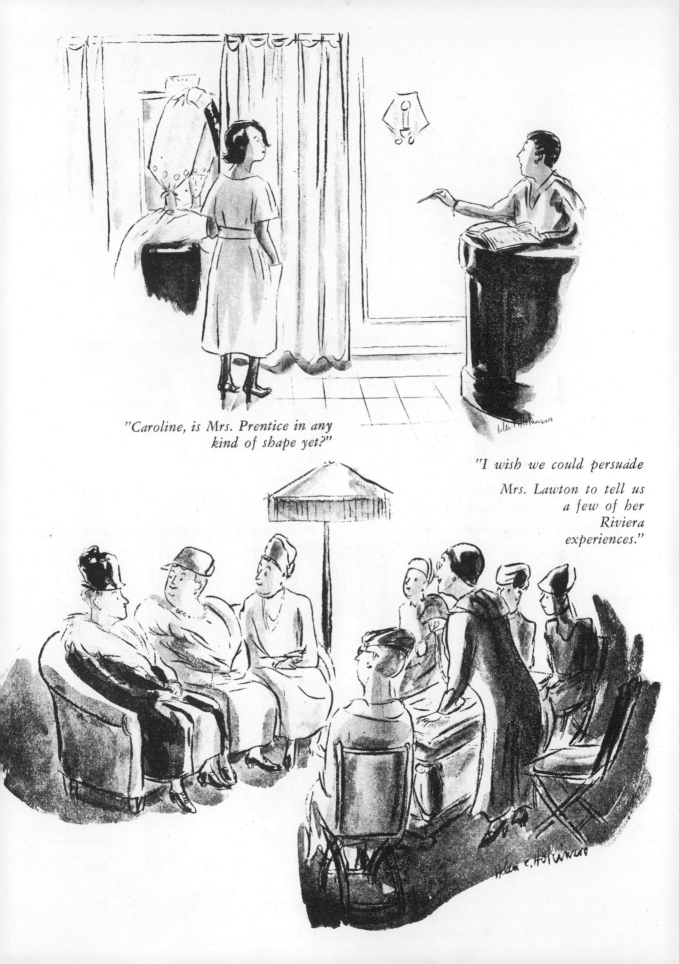

"Caroline, is Mrs. Prentice in any
kind of shape yet?"

"I wish we could persuade

Mrs. Lawton to tell us
a few of her
Riviera
experiences."

"*Well, I would never allow myself to become infatuated with royalty!*"

"*And you really want me to be Lady Macbeth?*"

"This is the one the guidebook says is so homelike, Momma."

"They practically had to <u>shoo</u> me out of Gimbels."

"*What do they call it when they take everything out of a lobster and then put it all back again?*"

"*Are you flowery or spicy?*"

"Mopsie and I are getting terribly fat, up in Darien."

SUMMER DOG SHOW

• •

"Now promise not to disappoint Mother in the ring!"

"They're going to feel sick when they see Wissahickon Laddie!"

"Rita, why <u>couldn't</u> you have held your head up? I never was so ashamed of you!"

"One small Buck Rogers twenty-fifth-century gun, please."

"Oh, I don't want the life of _anybody_."

*"Did I ever tell you that my sister was the first person in Germantown
to let chrysanthemums sprawl?"*

Really, Mr. Resoro, I think I'm entitled to a <u>little</u> consideration,
after the way I introduced zucchini to Englewood."

"Which is the best one for curing a cold?"

"I hear you have to make up to these judges."

Birthday party

A friend in the offing

*"What did you think of
the second movement?"*

"Hurry up!"

SATURDAY MORNINGS AT CARNEGIE

"I just want to show you what I'm up against."

"Remember, Mrs. Gurney, there's an element of mystery

"What ever happened to those inexpensive little islands off the coast of Spain?"

"Is there anyone here who knows anything about books?"

"On your toes tonight, everybody! The Bridgeport 'Post,' the Norwalk 'Hour,' and the Stamford 'Advocate' are all here!"

"Oh, he'll get used to it."

"Could you hide this for me until I get a dividend check?"

"Just how funny is this Milton, Berle?"

"I'm Mrs. Chester Frye and this is my friend Mrs. Goodly. We're from Manhasset, Long Island, and, frankly, we're just a pair of old snoops."

"It's awfully good so far. The first victim is a disagreeable cook."

"But if you married a man named Kimball the year you got out of college, what on earth did you do with Herbert Lundquist?"

"I think the judges ought to be told that Harriet did it all with her left hand."

"Oh, now Mrs. Stokely, surely you can suggest centuries of oppression better than that."

"When you say artists and writers eat here
do you mean the food is funny?"

"It's the same old story. Everything I hate is coming up
and everything I like _isn't_ coming up!"

"If this were only Venice, we could have haggled over the price."

"Do you mind if I copy the recipe off the bottom of this waffle iron?"

"Have you a treatment that includes lying down?"

*"What would you suggest for a small group of ladies
who meet every Tuesday to do needlepoint?"*

"Do you lick or do I lick?"

"Arthur, what do you suppose! Helena Rubinstein is going to let me come in and spend the whole day."

"Just amuse yourselves, everybody. I've got to tinker some more with these Sazeracs."

"I want to enlist your help in getting a charming little bride out of West Fourth Street."

"You mean I can't take off $16.48 for telegrams to congressmen?"

"Well! I certainly am finding out things about Charles the Second."

"My friends tell me I never make a very good first impression."

"Now let me see—champagne goes about three inches to the right of the knife, doesn't it?"

"Sometimes I'm afraid President Truman grins as much as President Roosevelt did."

"Where is whatever is reduced fifty per cent?"

"You know, I've often thought
I'd try _my_ hand at poetry."

"Of course, when I say farm, I don't mean cows
or chickens or anything like _that_."

"I don't see how you boys tell each other apart!"

"Sometimes I think Schrafft's
doesn't _care_ about calories."

I was the vivid one of the famil

I know this much—it isn't every day in the week that Lewis Gannett goes stark, staring mad."

"But why don't you become a Democrat and <u>enjoy</u> politics?"

Suppose you do fall down. That's how you meet people."

"Of course. Peter Rabbit is always very dependable."

"She's very like her father and has something of his sense of humo

"I had a little fight with Lord & Taylor last year, but we're friends now."

"The first couple of chapters are her babyhood and so on, but after that she really gets _going_."

"I suppose _they're_ going South, as usual."

"Lieutenants and captains like to get married, but majors just don't seem to care."

"Have you a wine that would be at home with an omelet?"

"If we get separated, look for me in the cyclamens."

"I go to all the trouble of driving these anemones from Babylon, and what do they do? They hang their heads!"

"Do you really think it's playing fair to shellac a pussy willow?"

"I'm terribly nervous. In just a few minutes, I'm going to be judged by Mrs. C. Monford Cole."

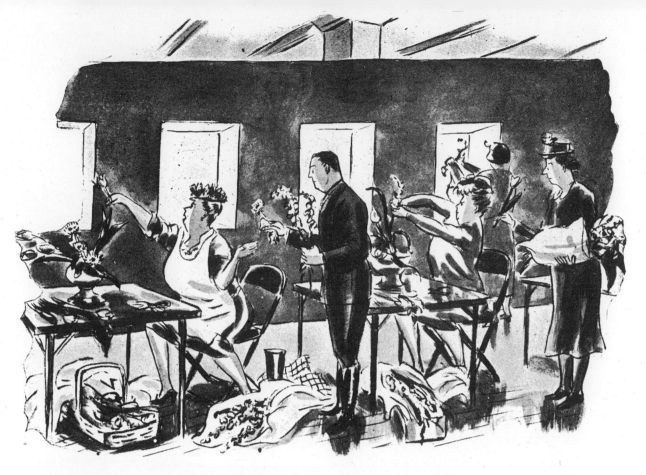

"Calendula . . . snapdragon . . . chicken wire . . . nippers . . ."

*"I want to achieve the effect
of a sombrero carelessly thrown down."*

*"But we can't go back
to the Waldorf with a rake!"*

"*I want to surprise my husband with one of those little red caps that lure deer.*"

"*...at reminds me—I have some jet put away in the attic.*"

"All he gives you is a corpse, a blood-spattered monkey wrench, and a will, and you carry on from there."

"You'd love my Dr. Brodie. His creed is rest, rest, rest, and more rest."

"What birds do you think make the best tenants?"

"I want to look as if I had stumbled accidentally into the twentieth century."

"Would you be angry, George, if I become *terribly* interested in pewter?"

"I want something that anybody
in Larchmont can find him in unexpectedly."

"We'll *murder* them, won't we, Mr. Briggs?"

"Which helps Great Britain the mos
tweeds or whiske

"Now, let's make Somerset
Maugham proud of us!"

"Just what is it you don't like about
the October Fantasy salad?"

"Well, let's see. Is your husband the lusty, swashbuckling type?"

"Well, of course, why Barbara Hutton got tired of Cary Grant is the mystery of the ages."

"It seems to have gone downhill terribly—last summer they always put a teaspoonful of sherry in the consommé."

"Get them on the phone again, Parker, and tell them the noisemakers haven't got here yet."

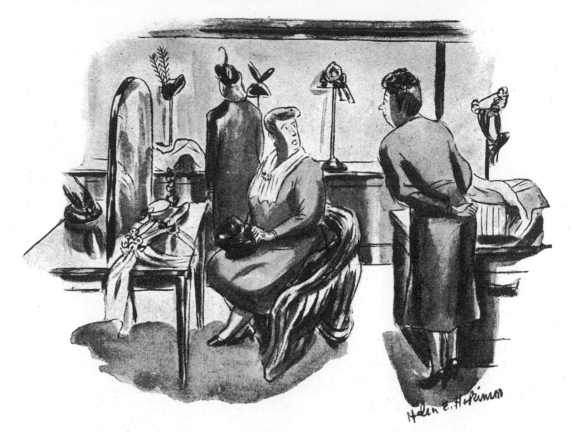

"Primarily, I want a head covering."

"Well, of course a really good sex maniac is always hard to find."

"This is the first time we've ever really <u>mixed</u> with other dogs."

*"I hate to ask you to take it
back, Miss Annette, but several people at Town Hall giggled."*

"Would you mind nudging me at a quarter to five?"

"I don't think she even <u>begins</u> to grasp Sartre."

*"It happened like this. One day
Miss Arden was looking at a beautiful sunset . . ."*

"You can't trust them, though. They spread."

*"Guess what, Herbert! I've just found
out that I danced with Dr. Kinsey thirty years ago!"*

*"Yoo-hoo, children! When I count ten I want someone
to name a beautiful flower."*

"Harvey, they want to do me from head to toe."

"Of course, all we've got is a fairly large fire escape."

"Do we look like maple people?"

"There must be something
wrong. I'm sure I weigh more than two and a half pounds."

"And now let's see if we can do the second act without bumping into anything."

"Isn't it about time for Massachusetts to begin?"

*"Suppose I tell you the kind
of life I lead, and then you suggest something."*

"I *thought* I recognized a Theatre Guild face."

"Oh, I stopped being afraid of Harper's Bazaar years ago."

"One nice thing about Schrafft's is, everybody else will look tired too."

"Which Van Doren was it I enjoyed so much?"

"I've decided to give atoms a rest for a few weeks."

*"Before we begin, I want you to remember
that you all revolve around the neurotic stepson."*

"*For he's a jolly good fellow, for he's a jolly good fellow . . .*"

"We've been so fortunate ever since we've been married. We've always had a thrush!"

"Approach, women of Athens!"

"A baby right here on Fifth Avenue! Isn't this an amazing city!"

"Suppose you was called upon to defend a woman's honor."

*"Which is the play
that we read deserves
the whole town's immediate and rapt attention?"*

"When I was a girl I
was so crazy about Napoleon
my father was worried."

"I'm hungry. What about you?"

"It has been moved that our recording secretary send a summary of today's discussion to Marshal Tito. Do I hear a second?"

"We raised it from one of the canary's
seeds. We'd always wondered what they were like."

"What a pity Mrs. Thompson is the way she is."

"Did you know that the stock-market page has a very clever column that tells everybody exactly what to invest *in?*"

"What I really wanted was something for an <u>older</u> dog."

"Perhaps I ought to explain that we're beginning to think about boys."

"But I thought people only went to Wisconsin on business."

"It's my birthday, and my husband said to get the works."

"Don't forget I want to come back by way of my sister-in-law."

"The room clerk assured me that all the animals here will run away from me."

"It gives me great pleasure to announce that the rummage sale will definitely result in John Charles Thomas."

"How does your skin react to secret ingredients?"

"Has our convoy to Mt. Vernon gone by here?"

*"It has to be large enough
for two birds who are very much in love."*

*"I want you to give me your solemn promise not to bolt
the Republican Party without having a heart-to-heart talk with me first."*

"*By the way, when we talk to my husband about Westport, maybe we'd better just not mention the artists.*"

"It is unfortunate that our treasurer moved to another town without explaining anything."

"I always mistrust them when they take a lot of prizes."

"Is it true that the White Mountains have been going downhill?"

"But isn't there some sort of <u>mock</u> gin?"

"I forgot the exact address, but you'll know the house because the first-floor
drapes, are dark blue with little white chrysanthemums."

"Well, if I were President of the United States, I wouldn't give jobs to everybody I play cards with."

PAPER SALVAGE

"I thought a few flowers would brighten up the place."

"Well, this man and this woman go off into the woods to live with nothing but the clothes on their backs. It's awfully interesting, but you'll be exhausted."

"Have you driven the new Buick with wizard control?"

"But Madam President, I think we should all take turns at entertaining people like Thornton Wilder."

"How is your sense of humor today, Mrs. Ridgely?"

"And now, shall we make one little concession to winter?"

"I'm going to send you the most wonderful Swede for your arthritis."

"You can see my problem—there's no mystery."

"Did you ever happen to hear of such a thing as 'Glamour?'"

"Would the Fifty-ninth Street Longchamps be crowded?"

"He wants to whisper something."

"We used to know some people who had a formal garden, but they drank."

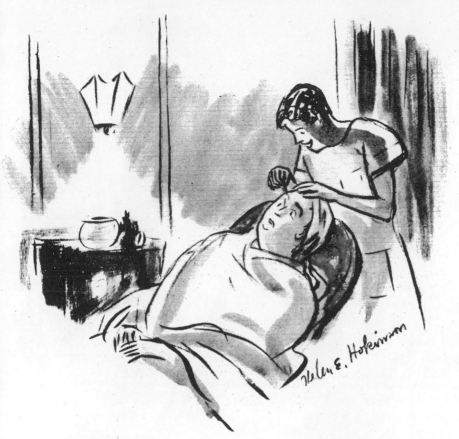

*"There **isn't** much I can do. This one eyebrow is naturally quizzical."*

"I'm afraid I bit off more 'Robert E. Lee' than I could chew."

"I know you're all as sorry as I am that the Chinese shadow plays last Saturday failed to bring out the husbands."

"Do you suppose I really could jolly my husband into the Black Hills?"

"If I weren't a guest of this club, I'd have some very
severe words to say about pruning laurel."

"Heavens! Who is that tall man standing beside Harriet?"

"Just say, 'Entertained a few members of the younger married set at bridge.'"

"Ahem. Oh, Cummings!"

"..., before I send you to this houseparty in Southampton, perhaps I ought to tell you a few things."

"I haven't any use for a detective who lets five or six people get killed."

"If it gives Madame a stomach we can take it out."

"Are we very far from civilization?"

"Any liquor, narcotics, tobacco, firearms, or explosives?"

"There's twelve cents due on John Marquand."

HELEN E. HOKINSON

WHEN his old friend William Archer died, Shaw, writing for once completely from the heart, confessed the impoverishment he felt at the idea of returning to an "Archerless London." "I still feel," he added, "that when he went he took a piece of me with him."

All of us, if only we have lived long enough, have been wounded beyond healing by similar losses. All of us, as the years slip by, face increasingly the problem of living with the abiding subtractions of death. These create gaps which cannot be filled and leave us suddenly lonely in the midst of crowds.

A few weeks back, when Helen Hokinson was among the fifty-five needlessly snuffed out in that air crash over Washington, thousands of us experienced once again this dreaded sense of deprivation even though ours had not been the privilege of knowing her personally. There is a difference, however, between the London without Archer to which Shaw returned and the America without Helen Hokinson in which we find ourselves. She is gone; abruptly, wastefully, tragically gone. Yet ours is by no means a Hokinsonless world. Her dying did not put an end to what we had all come to identify with her. That part of the American scene which she had staked off as her own can still be found everywhere, and its inhabitants will continue to bear her name so long as they present milliners with dilemmas and girdles with problems.

"My Best Girls" she called them, those denizens of women's clubs, beauty parlors, art galleries, summer resorts, and Lane Bryant, when she gave a title to one of her collections of *The New Yorker* drawings. This is what they were. Precisely that. Miss Hokinson's affection for her ample dowagers was so clear every time she caught their lines in hers that they were never offended by the fun she made of them. Symptomatic of the pleasure they took in her work was the letter she once received from a lady, a Hokinson lady of course, in Needham, Mass., who wrote, "More power to you and the girls. The more I grow to look like them, the more I love them."

What doubtless had equipped Miss Hokinson for dealing with American matrons in a manner not only unequaled but unexcelled is that in her art-school days, when she had left Chicago for New York, she studied dynamic symmetry. Her women were never to be confused with Clare Boothe's. They were stouts seeking in all matters to be stylish rather than worldings straining to be smart. Their sins of the flesh were dietary, not temperamental. They were — every mother's daughter of them — benevolent creatures waging a breathy, though losing, battle against the most innocent of appetites. If they carried more weight physically than they did intellectually, it was not because they failed to include culture among their pursuits.

Wherever their minds may have remained parked, those tiny feet of theirs, which terminated their plump legs, were forever carrying their bodies into book stores and museums, or leading them to lectures, matinees, or concerts. That is, of course, when Miss Hokinson's well-fed, well-bred, and thoroughly minked ladies were not molesting flowers, cajoling maids, tangling traffic, indulging in very private college reunions, massacring good liquor with unforgivable feminine additions, breaking down global problems into Westchester terms, or attempting to become sylphs again by submitting themselves to the costly Spartanism of Elizabeth Arden.

If they were resistant to the higher things, at least they were not dishonest in their reactions to them. Pretense was never one of their follies. At the Metropolitan's exhibition of French tapestries they were not embarrassed to ask an astonished guard, "Does it matter which end we do them from?" Confronted with abstract paintings in the Museum of Modern Art, one of them said, "I never know how far away to stand to make them look good." Picking up a volume in a book store, another inquired of the saleswoman, "Would this be all right for a friend who isn't interested in much of anything?" Turning to some companions, all of them as much alike as sister ships, still another summoned the honesty to complain during the intermission of a play, "It overwhelmed Brooks Atkinson, but it isn't overwhelming *me*." Or, listening to the Philharmonic, one of them, instead of parroting the program notes, offered as her sole comment: "I often wish I had kept up my mandolin lessons."

I have my reasons for citing these examples of that delectable off-beat in sense we associate with Miss Hokinson's world and work. All of these examples happen to be culled from her last book, "When Were *You* Built?" And that volume, significantly enough, was dedicated to James Reid Parker, whose captions, as she put it, "have inspired most of these drawings." In other words, as we are apt to forget, Miss Hokinson did not work alone. Mr. Parker was her silent partner. He was her idea man, and theirs one of the happiest of collaborations. Without any of the frictions of the lords of the Savoy, they found themselves as perfectly matched as Gilbert and Sullivan.

If Miss Hokinson's was the seeing eye, Mr. Parker's was the hearing ear. And what an ear it was — wonderful in its genius for seizing upon the absurd, wonderful in holding its nonsense close to truth, and also wonderful for the incredible accuracy with which it pounced upon *the* word among all other

words to make its satiric point without letting any blood. Take, for instance, the dowager saluting a street cleaner on Christmas day with "Joyeux Noel, my good man!" Or asking the captain of an ocean liner when it passes a cruiser, "Aren't we going to toot?" Or rising at a business meeting of a woman's club to announce, "I'm sorry, Madam President, there won't be any treasurer's report this month because we have a deficit." Or remarking to the instructor at a skating rink before taking to the ice, "I warn you, my right foot is a rebel."

The impact of such captions is instantaneous. They tell their own story and raise their own laughs. At least they seem to. But, as Mr. Parker would no doubt be the first to admit, they depend for their full relish upon the women — the Helen Hokinson women — we visualize as we read them.

Miss Hokinson's delineation of these women grew in certainty with the years. To realize this, one has only to follow her career from the first collection of her *New Yorker* drawings, "So You're Going to Buy a Book!" (1931), through "My Best Girls" (1941), to "When Were *You* Built?" (1948). During that richly productive period a type she had stumbled upon emerged as a species branded with her name. In no time this modest and retiring woman from Mendota, Ill., who had once done an unsuccessful comic strip for the *Mirror* called "Sylvia in the Big City," created a comic pattern cherished and admired by all Americans, including those from whom it was derived.

They were quite a group, these Hokinson dowagers. Funny, they certainly were. Yet they were also human, very human, and poignant, too. Their feelings belied their contours. They could not bring themselves to realize that their youth had left them. Regardless of the shadows they cast, they were girls at heart; girls who, though they had grown big, had never grown up. The calendar was unable to tarnish or remove their naivete. They were innocents both abroad and at home. One of the most ridiculous and touching of their characteristics was that their idea of mischief remained juvenile. They were worldings whom neither time nor exposure could make worldly. A reliable contributor to the hilarity they unfailingly provided was the contrast between their ingenuousness and the sophistication of their surroundings.

Economics was beyond them. The only figures with which they concerned themselves were their own, and even these they could not master. Their chief problem was idleness. Time hung heavy on their dimpled hands. Like all women who are unemployed, they had to seek employment in order to fill their empty days. Theirs was the usual solution. They were incessant shoppers. They were more intrigued with what covered their heads than with what filled them. Hats were their joy, and the search for them was a release from inactivity.

Gregarious as they were, Miss Hokinson's matrons were lonely, a fact which they confessed by squandering their affections on diminutive dogs. Even Philip Wylie could not have disliked these women since they were entirely innocent of momism. They were too busy babying themselves to mother anyone else. Foolish and self-indulgent as they were, they were never guilty of meanness. They were a friendly breed. This explains why they made so many friends. Miss Hokinson's fondness for them was transparent and contagious. Hers was the rarest of satiric gifts. She had no contempt for human failings. She approached foibles with affection. She could ridicule without wounding. She could give fun by making fun, and in the process make no enemies.

The New Yorker's loss is ours. It is saddening to realize Miss Hokinson will not draw her dowagers again. We, however, can derive some solace from the fact that the special world she discovered is still very much with us. Every time we see or chance to overhear pampered ladies of a certain size and vintage Helen Hokinson will be with us, too. She will be in our minds and also on our lips. The truth is she has become a living part of our vocabulary.

— JOHN MASON BROWN.

HELEN E. HOKINSON

Helen Elna Hokinson, the only daughter of Adolph and Mary Hokinson, was born in Mendota, Illinois, in 1893. She received a public-school education and subsequently studied at the Academy of fine Arts in Chicago. Moving to New York, she tried to establish herself as a fashion illustrator, but without notable success. At the same time she and Alice Harvey did a short-lived comic strip, "Sylvia in the Big City," for the N. Y. Daily Mirror. Continuing her education at the Parson School of Design, Miss Hokinson studied under Howard Giles, an enthusiastic advocate of Hambidge's theory of Dynamic Symmetry. The Hambidge principles impressed her greatly, and are reflected in all the work she did thereafter.

Miss Hokinson was studying under Giles when, in 1925, Harold. Ross and Raoul Fleischmann founded The New Yorker, and at the urging of some of her fellow-students she submitted a drawing to the new magazine. It was accepted. Two weeks later Miss Hokinson took another drawing to The New Yorker, and learned to her astonishment that the editors wanted her to bring in fresh material each Tuesday for consideration at the weekly art meeting. Their friendliness was especially comforting inasmuch as she had begun to realize that fashion illustrating was not her forte at all. Her early New Yorker drawings were unaccompanied by captions. Presently, however, the editors began to caption her work themselves, often originating ideas for her to complete and every month or so sending her on "covering art" assignments to sketch such assorted subjects as circuses, zoos, children's dancing classes, reducing salons, opera first nights, the varied events at the Grand Central Palace, and other metropolitan phenomena.

In 1931 a chance meeting with James Reid Parker led to a professional association that lasted for the next eighteen years, with Mr. Parker devising the situations and writing the captions for most of Miss Hokinson's drawings. In 1931, too, the first collection of the artist's work, entitled So You're Going To Buy a Book! after the manner of Clara Laughlin's travel series, was published by Minton Balch & Co. The three subsequent collections of her drawings — My Best Girls (1941), When Were You Built? (1948), and The Ladies, God Bless 'Em! (1950) — have been published by E. P. Dutton & Co.

As early as 1929 Miss Hokinson had formed the habit of dividing her time between an apartment in New York and a house in Connecticut. The winters she spent in New York; the rest of the year she lived in Fairfield County — at first in a secluded cottage in Silvermine, and then in a pleasant studio on the Wilton property of Mr. and Mrs. Elmer A. Sperry, Jr.

On November 1, 1949, Miss Hokinson drove her car from Wilton to La Guardia Airport, intending to return late that afternoon after spending a few hours in Washington. She had been invited to speak at a luncheon marking the opening of the capital's annual Community Chest drive, and although in general disinclined to leave Connecticut, even for a day's shopping in New York, she had accepted. As the plane in which she was traveling approached the National Airport, all aboard were killed in a collision that still ranks as one of the worst disasters in the history of civil aviation.

Miss Hokinson's body was buried in Mendota.

HELEN

by   JAMES REID PARKER

In 1931 that portion of Nineteenth Street which lies betwen Irving Place and Third Avenue was, as it is today, one of the pleasantest blocks in New York City. Generously tree-shaded, and with a variety of attractively remodeled houses, it includes a small, co-operatively-owned building of studio apartments. Helen Hokinson lived in this building, just around the corner from my own apartment on Gramercy Park. A friend of mine named Gladys Telfer told me this, adding that inasmuch as Miss Hokinson and I both contributed to *The New Yorker* it seemed too bad that we had never met. Gladys, who combines friendliness with efficiency, arranged for us to call on the artist one evening. Although I admired Helen Hokinson above all the other members of her profession, I was secretly fearful that the coming encounter would prove disillusioning. Not that I expected her to look like her drawings; rather, I was half-prepared to meet a worldly creature from the pages of *Harper's Bazaar*. She would be reclining on a chaise longue and would languidly wave a formidable cigarette holder as she uttered devastating witticisms in a bored tone, or so I feared. Women like that were the fashion just then.

The only part of this alarming notion that came true was the chaise longue, on which a slender woman with frightened hazel eyes and an untidy hairdo sat stiffly, twisting and mangling a tiny handkerchief in a fever of embarrassment. She appeared to be in her thirties. Her complexion, normally ruddy in the Scandinavian manner — she later told me that she was of Swedish descent and that her family had spelled its name Haakonson until her father's time — grew more and more vivid as we sat there, each of us unsuccessfully trying to hit on a topic that might be of general interest. Although Gladys had done her best, on the face of it her well-intentioned scheme of introducing the two neighbors appeared to have been a mistake.

That evening I acquired a few scraps of information about Miss Hokinson: she had lived for a while at the Smith Club, which at one time had been open to girls who were not alumnae, and had formed some warm friendships there; she regarded Hambidge's theory of Dynamic Symmetry as much more than an art fad, and in fact had made it the very foundation of her work; although she hadn't traveled much, she had spent several months working in Paris, and had loved sketching the street life; she hadn't read extensively, but she liked Trollope and Gaboriau; she shared her apartment with an elderly Canadian friend, a Miss Henderson. All this was interesting, but the Helen Hokinson of the drawings simply didn't seem to be in the room with us.

I happened to mention that in a story on which I was working there were two suburban matrons who talked, it seemed to me, the way some of her women might. Miss Hokinson asked what sort of things I was having them say, and I quoted a few lines of dialogue. She stopped twisting her handkerchief. With a sigh she remarked that one of the lines in particular would have made a good caption for a drawing and that the situation was exactly the kind of thing she liked to do. I told her to go right ahead because my women could just as easily be saying something else. Soon after this we again found ourselves at a conversational dead end, and presently Gladys and I departed.

One evening about a week later Miss Hokinson phoned me to say that *The New Yorker* had bought the drawing built around the line I had given her. I told her that I felt more than honored to have a share in a Hokinson drawing, and when she asked whether I had any other fragments she could use, I promised to rummage through my desk and see. It was then that she told me about her own filing system — rough sketches, idea notes, and illustrations torn out of magazine and newspaper ads all methodically arranged under such headings as "Automobiles," "Children," "Dogs," "Elections," "Flower Shows," and so on. The usefulness of such a scheme was so apparent to me that

I decided to start a similar file myself instead of allowing random notes jotted on the backs of envelopes to accumulate in my desk, between book pages, and in bureau drawers.

"I keep hearing Gilbert and Sullivan," Miss Hokinson remarked with interest. "Is it a radio, or are they records?" I said that they were records, and explained that I owned the various d'Oyly Carte albums. "Will you play some of them for me sometime?" she asked, without a trace of the diffidence she had displayed the week before. I said I'd be glad to, and asked her whether she'd like to hear some of them then and there. She came right over.

We spent a delightful evening listening to *Iolanthe* and talking about what it was like to work for *The New Yorker*. We agreed that we set great store by the judgment of our editor, Harold Ross. "When he pencils 'Not funny' in the margin of a drawing and I look at it later, I generally realize to my horror that it *isn't*," Miss Hokinson confided. After *Iolanthe* we were on a pleasantly friendly basis. She told me that a lot of people called her "Hokie," which somehow suggested to me a probably untrue picture of young women boisterously pulling taffy in kimono-filled rooms at the Smith Club. I told her I liked the name "Helen" better. As we talked I noted that the things she spoke about with sudden animation and lilting enthusiasm were always extremely specific, not general. Not the crowd but a face in the crowd, not the bouquet but a single flower in the bouquet. There was new life and color in her voice whenever she spoke of the *minutiae*, literally the most minute details, of anything that appealed to her.

I liked, too, the old-fashioned, rather Cranfordish adjectives that she tended to use every now and again. I remember her describing Ross that evening as having an "engaging" guffaw. This word, which is not often used in casual conversation, charmed me.

As I was about to take Helen home, she produced a blue slip of paper and said that it was a "commission." She explained that *The New Yorker* always paid a fee to anyone who suggested an idea for a drawing, and that she did the same thing herself when, as occasionally happened, someone gave her an idea direct. I was considerably embarrassed, and said something mildly jocose to the effect that I could accept only "books, flowers, candy, or gloves" from the members of the opposite sex. Helen didn't get the point of this Victorian conceit and merely looked baffled. I was afraid that she might resume the long silences and the handkerchief twisting, and in a moment of inspiration I suggested that we use the check to blow ourselves to dinner and the theater. Helen thought this a wonderful solution, and at once inquired practically whether I had any more ideas she could use for drawings.

"As a matter of fact, I do," I said. "Something I overheard on a bus this week. You're welcome to draw it if you want to."

She drew it and *The New Yorker* bought it, and thereafter I gave Helen material regularly — both in the form of notes I kept accumulating for possible inclusion in stories, and of situations and lines that I simply invented. For about a year the commission checks obliged us to dine together and go to the theater once or twice a week — an agreeable predicament. Then, our collaboration having assumed these proportions, we entered into a business agreement and set aside Friday afternoons and evenings as definite work periods, during which we examined each other's files, outlined future work for Helen, and studied rejections to see how they might be made acceptable. Naturally the magazine itself continued to send ideas to Helen, as before, and once in a while she was able to pluck something really excellent from her fan mail. As a result, she was never without a supply of usable material.

Helen herself was extremely good at thinking up subjects for the magazine covers she did in water color, but less so at devising situations with lines. Mr. John Mason Brown accurately describes Helen as having had a Seeing Eye; visual perception, rather than aural, was her specialty — so much so that she sometimes gave a downward glance while crossing a lawn and halted to pick the four-leaf clover she had idly detected in the dense carpet at her feet. It may seem a *non sequitur,* but this reminds me that the instant Helen first saw Mae West on the screen, she nudged me and said, "Look at the nostrils! You have to go to Greek sculpture to find nostrils modeled like that."

Investigating the city with Helen was fascinating for a great many reasons. She was forever sketching people in parks, in restaurants, in the lobbies of hotels and business buildings, during theater intermissions, at the special events held in Madison Square Garden and Grand Central Palace, and in fact wherever we went. A man bent down to tie a shoelace, a woman rummaged through her purse for the elusive bus fare, an impatient youth scanned a hotel lobby for his date, a woman deliberated over a tray of pastries, a man studied his new haircut in a slot-machine mirror, a father hurried a reluctant child past a pet-shop window — and with her soft Eberhard pencil Helen quickly drew a few wonderful lines on her pocket-size sketch pad. Meanwhile, I kept jotting down the notes about people, places, and situations that I use in my own trade. Details. Sometimes I wrote down the words I heard spoken by the people Helen was sketching. This material either resulted in drawings or found its way into stories or simply remained in our files for possible use some day. I still think Helen's rough sketches as eloquent as her finished drawings, and in many cases more so. (A rough Helen once did when we were poking around Lewis & Conger's hardware displays I considered slightly *too* eloquent. "Reid, would you mind taking hold of the handles of that lawn-mower?" Helen had said. "Pretend you're pushing it. I want to get the position of a man's arms and the angle of his back." She got rather more than that. When I stiffly re-marked that it seemed to me she had needlessly exaggerated the double chin and the receding hairline, Helen said with professional pride that she always tried to draw exactly what she saw, an announcement that failed to cheer me. She squinted at me and at the rough, did a bit of erasing, and went to work again. She's sorry for what she's done and she's going to make everything all right, I thought. "I'm changing the eyes a bit so as to add your *worried* look," Helen said in a businesslike tone as she added one more facet to the already appalling jewel.)

Our jaunts around New York were enlivened for me, in the early years of our association, by my inability to predict just what sort of costume Helen would wear. Her blouses and scarves were especially colorful, and she was addicted to gay Romany combinations of orange, pink, scarlet, magenta, and cobalt, occasionally enhancing the effect with a chrome-yellow hat and a cherry-colored sweater. I recall her complaining once, when we were in some public place or other, that she had been waiting for ages to draw a certain unsuspecting woman — "but I can't ever get started because she keeps turning and looking at me." I said, "Of course she does. She probably can't make up her mind whether you're a double rainbow or an aviary of tropical birds." Helen giggled. "Why, Reid!" she said. "The clothes I'm wearing today are comparatively subdued!" As the years passed, Helen's wardrobe became much more conservative and also extremely fashionable, and she increasingly chose the grays and pastels that went so well with her hair as it turned silver. Personally, I missed the old abandon.

The chief reason it was so entertaining to work with Helen — or, equally, to be with her and *not* to work — was that the spontaneity of her enthusiasm had a tonic quality and, since we reacted alike to so many things, often expressed a rich delight in a visual experience that I myself would have felt but would have been slower to voice. (And no doubt would have voiced more pedantically.) When Helen said "*Look!*" in a tone of the utmost excitement, it generally meant that she had discovered a tiny detail of some kind that she hoped I would enjoy. "The way that man is smiling," she might add. Then I would see what she meant, that the smile was actually a smirk, brimful of complacence. Her powers of observation were extraordinary beyond telling, and her talent for helping you to see what she herself saw was a great gift. It was as if the very genius of comedy took you by the hand and showed you things. But if Helen regarded the small frustrations and humiliations of life as comic, as her drawings prove that she did, I must record that she never for one moment lacked respect for the fact that to the person involved they are always deadly serious, if only temporarily. For example, when I told her that a woman leaving the French Tapestries exhibit at the Metropolitan had said sharply to her young son, "Can't you remember *anything* except the blood that ran out of the horse?" I knew that Helen at once sympathized with what must certainly have been the mother's private thoughts: "Is he going to grow up to be a murderer? If I try to talk to my husband about it, he'll only laugh. It's that damn school, that's what it is! Coming to see these tapestries has been an absolute waste of time. And my feet hurt, and we've still got to go to the oculist and Rogers Peet before we can take a train back to Mamaroneck!" Helen understood perfectly, and as she worked at her drawing board, bringing the harassed mother to life, the artist no doubt murmured compassionately, "Cheer up, lady!"

I am tempted to list Helen's special interests during the years I knew her, but the task is too overwhelming for me to accomplish in full. I have already mentioned Gilbert and Sullivan. Helen conceived an idea of forming a club of twelve to listen to records of an opera every other week. This club was hugely popular, and so many guests began to appear that we had to restrict each member to bringing no more than one guest at a time to Helen's studio, where the parties were held. We took to reading the dialogue aloud between records, and I still recall with pleasure Gilbert W. Gabriel's spirited performance of Sir Despard Murgatroyd in *Ruddigore* and also the dramatic critic's confession that he would so much rather have achieved his reputation *on* the stage instead of facing it. Helen's other likes included backgammon, the French Impressionists, the Christmas carol programs of the English singers, Arno and Mary Petty, nasturtiums ("I wish they had named a nasturtium after me instead of an orchid"), Ray Bolger's dancing, wildflowers, Shakespeare, detective stories, the Connecticut back roads at dusk, and bridge. Bridge and politics constituted our chief areas of disagreement. After our feelings about these two subjects had become known to each other, however, we never alluded to either of them again.

Connecticut was Helen's home for much of every year. When I first visited her in the country, I found her living in an idyllic woodland retreat, a rambling pink cottage that she shared with the Miss Henderson I mentioned earlier and with a delightful and remarkably talented businesswoman, Lulu Fellows. Despite her triumphs as an executive, the latter had a taste for quiet country living. But poor Lu got to the cottage for weekends only, and always arrived in a state of near-collapse. I was invited to this haven fairly often, and my first recollections of it are closely bound up with my gratitude to my hostesses for the brand of aid they administered to a young man who hated working in New York in the summer and who repeatedly found himself becoming involved in temporary romantic attachments. Helen viewed these complications with tolerant amusement, and she and Miss Henderson and Lu provided the best entertainment in the world: hearty bacon-and-egg breakfasts, backgammon at reasonable stakes, swimming in a natural woodland pool with a delectable edging of Chinese forget-me-nots and cinnamon fern and with a mossy, beech-shaded stretch near by that served as an outdoor living room, drives to visit such artist-neighbors as *The New Yorker's* Perry Barlow and Alice Harvey, and the fun of doing congenial work in the happiest of settings. After a couple of such summers of merely tasting Connecticut now and then, I was able to rearrange my New York duties so that I could rent, and spend the greater part of each week in, a cottage not far from Helen's and one that gave its tenants riparian rights to the opposite side of her woodland pool. Thereafter Helen's guests and mine mingled amiably, often joining forces for picnic lunches, and whenever it was necessary Helen and I could confer about a drawing on very short notice. We worked together on quite a few advertising jobs, and for a year or so did a monthly panel called "The Dear Man" for the *Ladies' Home Journal,* which good-naturedly consented to serve as a show window in which Helen could demonstrate regularly that she could draw the male of the species as deftly as she did the female. (She had drawn men for *The New Yorker* ever since its first year, of course, but the continuing Woman's Club series that I had devised for her in 1933 seemed to have fixed her in the public mind as an artist who drew women only, and women of a certain class, age, and temperament, at that.)

In 1938 I took a trip to Alaska. I felt that the time had come for me to resign an academic appointment I had held for a number of years and to make my work much more "portable." It was while I was on this trip that Helen and I began what an editorial in the New York *Herald-Tribune* later called our "unique, mostly long-distance collaboration." At least, that was when we began the "long-distance" part of it. We agreed that we knew each other's files pretty thoroughly, and hoped that we could carry on as effectively as ever if we exchanged daily postcards, Helen telling me what she had been sketching and I sending her suggestions as to how to use the material, with situations for drawings outlined and with captions provided. On one of the first postcards I wrote: "I heard a man querulously ask one of the *Princess Alice's* dining-saloon stewards whether anyone had found the bottle of pills he had left behind after breakfast. 'They were dollar-and-a-half pills,' the man grumbled. Remember your sketch of Mrs. B. looking triumphant about her first grandchild? You could draw the same woman, equally triumphant, saying to a luncheon companion at Schrafft's, 'My dollar-and-a-half pills are doing me *so* much good!'" The postcard method worked admirably, and thereafter I forwarded material to Helen with consistent regularity from Alaska, Europe, Bermuda, or wherever I happened to be.

When I was in New York or Connecticut we resumed the Friday sessions, of course, and after I married, my wife and I generally dined with Helen on that day, or she with us, following the afternoon conference. But no longer having a home in New York, I relied heavily on the postcard method, especially during the four years I was in the Army. It was always a source of refreshment to me to pick up a card and a pen and forward observations to Helen and to receive hers in return. In correspondence as in conversation, Helen was likely to begin excitedly, "Guess what!" and then came a description of whatever had enthralled her most recently. Sometimes told, sometimes drawn. Perhaps Helen had detected a bleary-eyed bum fishing the book-review section of a Sunday paper out of a trash receptacle; or possibly she had just been introduced to a woman who had had her dog psychoanalyzed; or Katharine Cornell had dropped in for a few minutes "just the way people do in Mendota!"; or a clerk in Brentano's had assured her that there really *was* such a person as Louis Bromfield.

Realizing that somewhere in this memoir I should mention the fact that Helen was not one to build up a large stock of general information, I believe that this is where I must bring it in. Her formal education had been scant, and punditical conversation not only puzzled her but made her uneasy. I have seen Hokinson admirers try to be richly allusive and clever when in her presence and merely succeed in frightening her instead of making the hoped-for good impression. About Mr. Bromfield: I had used the novelist's name in a caption in which a Garden Club member rose to ask a guest speaker whether or not Louis Bromfield was "pro-earthworm." (The great earthworm controversy has now somewhat abated in gardening circles.) Helen smiled perfunctorily and inquired who Louis Bromfield was. I explained about Malabar Farm and all that, but Helen said in a skeptical tone that she didn't believe he was a writer whose name would be familiar to anyone. In this paragraph, which while incidental is necessary to an understanding of Helen, I should add that Helen almost never read a line of text in *The New Yorker*. After noting the cover and the drawings, she methodically put each copy away in an old chest. (The writings of several of the magazine's contributors she liked very much, especially Mr. Thurber's, but she generally read them in book form.) Helen once asked me not to tell anyone at the office that she had never read *The New Yorker*, and until now I have refrained from making the admission. I mention it here only because I think it has a certain bearing on the first sentence in this paragraph. After all, that Helen was not much addicted to modern reporting — she examined newspapers and the weekly and monthly magazines with a kind of fretful haste, pausing chiefly when she came to a picture — seems to me to detract not at all from the fact that she observed and then drew with innate comprehension and exquisite skill so much of the America of her day.

Helen's many friends — Helen Mobert, Lu Fellows, Alice Harvey, Hermine Deutsch, Perry and Dorothy Barlow, Walter Cook, Dorothy Osborn, Mr. and Mrs. Hawley Truax, Ruth Woodward, Elizabeth Schumann, Helen Sperry, Mrs. George Bellows, Margaret Goldsmith, and my wife, to name some of the people of whom Helen was especially fond — will correctly point out that I am omitting or barely touching upon various points that would help to explain Helen Hokinson, but then this hardly pretends to be a complete psychoanalytical study. The large birthmark on her neck must have been responsible for much of her early shyness and also for the tendency to alternate between openness and secretiveness that most of her intimates noted now and again. (Nothing of importance was ever involved, and I feel reasonably sure that the latter habit, a natural formula for self-protection that she had developed in childhood, never affected any of her major friendships.) Helen was a Christian Scientist of quiet and abiding faith, and when an operation for a thyroid condition became necessary in the Forties, she submitted to it with a wryness that masked the genuine sorrow of one who felt that she had somehow been lacking in spiritual strength. I believe that Christian Science gave her an inward life and a self-confidence that the birthmark had made her yearn for; it helped her to face the world with courage. It took a long time for Helen to realize that people gave almost no thought to the discoloration. One day I asked her, in all innocence, why she kept on wearing a scarf or something about her neck after the weather had turned warm. She blushed violently and with an effort at casualness spoke of the mark. "Nobody except you ever notices it," I told her with perfect truth. In later years Helen succeeded in forgetting about it almost entirely, which I consider a triumph worth telling.

Some mention should be made of Helen, an enthusiastic businesswoman, bargaining regularly for better contracts. Barring a few minor differences of opinion now and then, Helen's relations with *The New Yorker* were always extremely happy, thanks to Ross's instinctively intelligent editing, Hawley Truax's great tact, and Helen's underlying knowledge that she was dealing with people who loved her and who wanted to protect her interests as well as their own.

And then there were the odd little legends about herself that Helen encouraged interviewers to perpetuate, most notably the one about her never having thought her drawings funny until her fellow art students and her instructor had chuckled over them and urged her to send something to the newly founded *New Yorker*. This was, quite simply, not true. As far back as her highschool days, when she was sketching her classmates and other fellow-townsmen, she had discovered that there is always a touch of comedy in the truth. Helen saw the comedy — and the pathos, too. (Caption under a drawing in an old notebook: "This is Lucy trying to make a 'hit' with the football captain!") But the first time Helen ever was interviewed, by George S. Chappell, she guessed correctly that naivete would make good copy, and thereafter she became on innumerable occasions a not-so-simple child who lightly drew her breath and felt her life in every limb. For Emma Bugbee, Dorothy Dunbar Bromley, *Time* men, and many others. "Helen, someone really should spank you!" I said severely one day, after having been a witness at the most recent of these prankish sessions. "Why, Reid, I don't know what you mean," Helen said primly. "You probably didn't read *The New Yorker's* story about Julia Peterkin being handed a pre-breakfast cup of coffee by a maid in the Southern mansion Mrs. Peterkin was visiting," I said. "The maid reported that after Mrs. Peterkin had gone to bed much earlier than was the household's custom, the hostess had paid her a very handsome compliment in the course of conversation with the other guests. Had compared her with a flower, in fact. As Mrs. Peterkin tells the story, the maid explained, 'She say you de bigges' posy she ever saw.'" Helen thought about this for a moment, and then broke into joyous and hysterical laughter. When she had calmed down, she remarked philosophically, "Well, you have to say *something* to interviewers, don't you?"

And the play. For several years before Helen died she had been fascinated by the notion that if a competent dramatist would write a play about the kind of women she drew, she would lend her name to it and it would be a big Broadway hit and then be sold to the movies for a large sum. Two or three playwrights, encouraged by Helen, tried their hands at the job, but their rough drafts struck her as being too farcical and too tainted with caricature. Liking Miss Nancy Hamilton's clever revue sketches, Helen invited this talented and theater-wise young woman to collaborate with her. Together they wrote a play which did not find favor with the managers to whom it was submitted. Helen decided to write a play on her own. She joined the New York Society Library and at the time of her death was busily engaged in studying the works of Barrett Clark, William Archer, Arthur Hopkins, and others who have written books about play construction. What had started out as a scheme to capture a bagful of Hollywood money had ended in an earnest ambition to write a truly worthy play for the stage. For two years the notion had captured her imagination to such an extent that at her death she had fallen far behind in meeting her *New Yorker* commitments. I think it entirely possible that in time she might have written a commercially successful play. No project had engrossed her so much, nor truly challenged her so much, since her encounter with Hambidge's Dynamic Symmetry some twenty-six years before. It is equally arguable that she might have failed, but I prefer to believe that she would have succeeded.

Helen's other friends may consider that what I have written is inadequate, as of course it is, but they will not quarrel with me when I say that she was one of the most extraordinarily generous women who ever lived. Helen's greatest pleasure was in the choosing of a present, not in the recipient's gratitude. Christmases and birthdays always brought the very things one wanted. Last year, when my wife and I came back from a spring in Europe to our island home off the coast of Massachusetts, my wife said, "I wish Helen could see this house! Some of the nicest things in it are things she's given us." And in the batch of waiting mail was a letter from Helen asking if she could come for a week in July.

Helen wasn't a great hand for visiting. In all the years I had known her, the total number of visits she had made were two, one to see Hannah Carpenter in Maine and one to see Miss Hamilton on Martha's Vineyard. Helen came to our island by plane. It was her first taste of air travel and she said it was so pleasant that she thought she'd accept an invitation to attend a Community Chest luncheon in Washington in the fall and go down and back by air. We inspected the garden and then the house, including the gifts she had sent us throughout the years. ("That's all wrong in this room," she said, critically inspecting one of her rugs. "Give it to somebody who has a room it'll go better in, Ruth, and let me try to find something that will harmonize properly with the flowers in the wallpaper.") After the tour Helen moaned, "Now I know what to give you people, but I'll never be able to because I don't know how to go about doing it. What you get the most pleasure out of is the garden, and I honestly believe the handsomest present I could ever give you would be a load of manure." This was just about true, but as Helen added, "That's where people who live in New York are at a disadvantage, you know. I can't just go into Bergdorf's and ask them to send some, wrapped as a gift." Helen presently discovered that we were making home-made peach ice cream in a borrowed Sears Roebuck freezer. "May I lick the dasher, and wouldn't you like a freezer of your own?" Helen asked.

She sent one, of course, as soon as she got back to Connecticut, and several other items she had a notion we might find useful. Our own private achievement in the gift-hunting line had been that we had found in Paris, and were reserving for the coming Christmas, the most appropriate possible bit of jewelry for Helen: a pin in the form of a palette with a half-circle of semi-precious stones representing the daubs of paint and with a pair of gold brushes thrust through the hole in the palette. I still wish we had slipped it into her hand before she stepped into the plane that took her away from our island. Helen's delight in a surprise was always so exuberant that it warmed your heart and made you want to go right out and hunt for something else that would please her.

She phoned me a few days before she was to go to Washington, "I'm not calling about business," she said. "I just felt like having a chat." Her playwriting problems were very much on her mind, and she described them at length. "By the way, I'm still trying to get rid of the ten pounds I put on at your house," she said at the end. "Tell Ruth. The sea air gave me such an appetite and the food was so wonderful that I succumbed and enjoyed myself like —" Helen groped for a phrase that would be sufficiently descriptive, and found one. "Like a *Hokinson* woman!" she said.

Having a few minutes to spare at La Guardia Airport, Helen sketched a man and a woman arguing with each other in the waiting room. "Can't we do something with these people?" she scribbled under the drawing, and posted it to me from the airport.

Of the next hour I need not write. Ross telephoned late that afternoon, when word from Washington had extinguished his last hope. Talking was hard for both of us.